· 59

Mig

The Superstar Pig

Colin and Jacqui Hawkins

FAMILY LEARNING

FAMILY LEARNING

from Dorling Kindersley

*The Family Learning mission is to support the concept
of the home as a centre of learning and to help families
develop independent learning skills to last a lifetime.*

Editors: Bridget Gibbs, Fiona Munro
Designers: Chris Fraser, Claire Ricketts

Published by Family Learning

Dorling Kindersley registered offices:
9 Henrietta Street, Covent Garden, London WC2E 8PS

VISIT US ON THE WORLD WIDE WEB AT:
http://www.dk.com

ISBN 0-7513-7174-2

Colour reproduction by DOT Gradations
Printed in Hong Kong by Wing King Tong

A CIP catalogue record for this book is
available from the British Library.

Have you heard about Miss Mig?
She got herself a brand new wig.
Now she's really made it big
as a famous TV pig!

Mig wears lots of
sparkly things,
bangles, beads
and glittery rings.
She really loves all things sweet –
but chocolates are her
favourite treat.

Chocolate for Mig,
the party-dress pig!

Lots of cake and pink ice-cream,
make Mig's life a super dream.
Every night she dines out late,
eating off a silver plate.
She's Miss Mig,
the superstar pig!

Mig the pig is superstar flash, spending lots and lots of cash. Every day she buys a new gown! She lives in style in the best house in town.

Mig relaxes by her pool,
looking really super cool.
Then she takes a little dip
with a fizzy drink to sip.
That's Miss Mig,
the superstar pig!

I'm Miss Mig,
the superstar pig.

Mig's cool...

...in her pool.

Mig's a star when she's afloat
on her own fantastic boat.
She likes to go on holiday
and sail to places
far away.

In her jet or in her car,
Mig is such a superstar.
Always smiling,
on the go,
ready for her
TV show!
That's Miss Mig,
the superstar pig!

THE MIG THE PIG SHOW

Every Saturday night
Mig's in the spotlight.
A TV show queen,
she fills up the screen.
"The show tonight is
big, big, big!"
says Miss Mig,
the superstar pig.

There's no business...

...like show business.

TV 3

"The first star of the show,
just watch him go!
It's Harry the horse,
who hoofs it, of course!
He'll dance on his toes
and then on his nose."

Next on the show is Mr O'Dare,
the amazing, cycling,
high-wire bear.
He stands on a chair,
while high in the air.
Oh, do take care,
Mr O'Dare!

On comes Chuck,
the daring duck.
He swings with ease
on a high trapeze,
eating Swiss cheese
and a pan of
green peas.

He juggles with fish
and a large glass dish.
That's Chuck,
the daring duck!

"Now, cheer as loud as you can,
I'm his biggest fan.
It's Jerome the giraffe
who makes us all laugh.
Give him a big clap,
he's a very funny chap,"
      says Miss Mig,
        the superstar pig.

What's the biggest ant?

An elephant.

Is your hair wet? There's a big drip under it.

How do you stop your nose from running? Stick your foot out and trip it up.

There was an old man from Peru who dreamed he was eating his shoe. He woke in a fright during the night, and found it was perfectly true!

"And now for
your delight,
the last act tonight.
It's Pat the cat
and his magic hat!"
He waves his wand,
a magic stick,
and ends the
show with his
best trick.

"Goodnight, everyone,
it's been such fun.
It's time to go –
it's the end of the show.

I didn't fall!
I love you all!

Thanks to Mr O'Dare,
the high-wire bear.

Chuck,
the daring duck.

I hung by my knees
on the flying trapeze.

Jerome the giraffe,
who makes us laugh.

*Whenever I spoke,
out came a joke!*

Pat the cat
and his
magic hat.

*I'm the cat
with the
magic hat.*

And, of course –
Harry the horse!

*I danced
on my toes
and then on
my nose.*

It's been a ball.
Goodbye. Goodbye.
I love you all,"
says Miss Mig,
the superstar pig.